D1231589

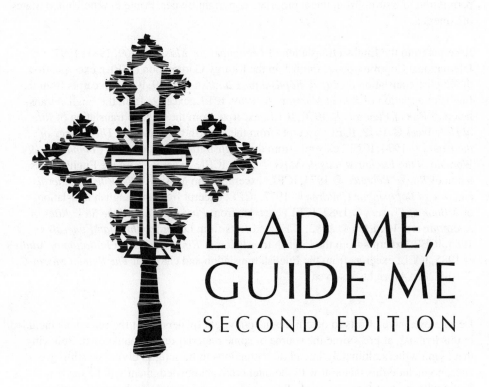

LEAD ME, GUIDE ME
SECOND EDITION

GIA PUBLICATIONS, INC.
CHICAGO

LEAD ME, GUIDE ME

Most Reverend Wilton D. Gregory, SLD
Archbishop of Atlanta
Honorary Chairman

Reverend Monsignor Raymond P. East
General Chairman

Robert J. Batastini
Senior Editor/Project Director

Advisory Committee

Most Rev. Wilton D. Gregory, SLD, Chairman, Most Rev. Edward K. Braxton,
STD, Rev. Msgr. Raymond P. East, Rev. Fernand Cheri, OFM, Rev. J-Glenn
Murray, SJ, Rev. Robert H. Oldershaw, Dr. James Abbington, Robert J. Batastini,
Marcia Berry, Derek Campbell, Beverly Carroll, Meyer Chambers, Richard
Cheri, Michael Cymbala, Kelly Dobbs-Mickus, Dr. Norah Duncan, IV,
Alec Harris, Edward Harris, Kenneth W. Louis, Eric Styles.

Editorial Core Committee

Dr. James Abbington
Marcia Berry
Richard Cheri
Dr. Norah Duncan, IV
Rev. Msgr. Raymond P. East
Sr. Joan Angela Edwards, SSM
Kenneth W. Louis
Rev. J-Glenn Murray, SJ

FOREWORD

As I reread the preface and the introductory articles from the first edition of *Lead Me, Guide Me*, once again I could not help but reflect in profound admiration upon the generosity and the talents of so many of those who were engaged in that pioneer effort to bring the music and spiritual vitality of African-Americans into a closer relationship and usage within the Catholic Church. Many of those who participated in the publication of the first edition of *Lead Me, Guide Me* have since fallen asleep in Christ, but I now trust that their splendid contributions will also inspire this second edition and that they will smile on our humble efforts. Clarence and Thea, Jim Lyke and Bede Abrams, Joe Francis, Leon Roberts, and Booker Ashe were all so deeply and personally dedicated to making this project a success, and their efforts were richly rewarded as *Lead Me, Guide Me* has now served the Church in the United States well for more than twenty-four years.

African-American spiritual music is classified among the great cultural treasures of our nation, and we gladly and enthusiastically share it with all who have been and continue to be inspired by its contributions. *Lead Me, Guide Me* is a compilation of a generous selection of that music arranged for use within the celebration of the Roman Catholic liturgy. As we Catholics now prepare to receive the third edition of the *Roman Missal* for the English-speaking world, it is most appropriate for a new edition of *Lead Me, Guide Me* to be issued to accompany that new book of Catholic prayer. Those blessed original collaborators have today been joined by a new generation of very capable colleagues in preparing this new text. They build on a solid foundation of faith and now present a worthy successor to that first effort.

While *Lead Me, Guide Me* was specifically developed with the particular liturgical needs of the African-American Catholic community in mind, it was never envisioned to be used exclusively in those parish communities. Other Catholics throughout our nation and beyond have made very effective use of this liturgical resource, and we anticipate that they, too, will welcome this newest edition. Music has a unique capacity to transcend cultures and races and provide a bridge to understanding other people through the vehicle of its combined words and melodies. That bridge-building was also a welcome benefit of the first edition of *Lead Me, Guide Me*, and I have every expectation that the entire Catholic community will welcome this new edition and find it a bridge from which the entire Church might glimpse the beauty and the spiritual depth of the soul of the people who composed and continue to cherish these songs of faith.

Most Reverend Wilton D. Gregory, SLD
Archbishop of Atlanta

PREFACE

It all began on December 11, 2002, when the advisory committee gathered in Chicago under the leadership of Archbishop Wilton D. Gregory. It was an inspiring all-day session that identified the need for, and set the direction of, the revision of *Lead Me, Guide Me: The African American Catholic Hymnal* (1987).

The core committee was assembled, and soon the work began. This committee met for two- and three-day work sessions spread over the next seven years. It is a tribute to the dedication of the very busy people on the core committee to note that all members were present for every meeting—no exceptions. As word of the impending revision of the *Roman Missal* became known, it was clear that the hymnal could not be published until such revisions were in place, thus stretching the project out for as many years as it has ultimately taken.

Much was learned from the experience of using *Lead Me, Guide Me* (1987) in parish worship for twenty years, and all of this experience informed the work of the committee. A comparison of the two editions will make it readily apparent that the second edition is more liturgically complete, broader in scope—both in the sheer number of items included and in the breadth of the materials represented—and more sophisticated in its editing, thus better representing the musical performance practices of the African American church.

Each member of the core committee brought his or her unique gifts to the project: the chairman, Msgr. Raymond P. East, an extraordinary pastoral sense; Rev. J-Glenn Murray, SJ, liturgical scholarship; Sr. Joan Angela Edwards, SSM, a knowledge of the music of Caribbean immigrants; Dr. James Abbington, an academic knowledge of African American church music; Marcia Berry, a lifetime of experience as a parish musician; Richard Cheri, liturgy and music workshop/conference organizer and parish musician; Dr. Norah Duncan IV, twenty-six years as cathedral music director with *Lead Me, Guide Me* in the pews; and Kenneth Louis, composer and arranger of music for the Black church, and parish musician.

The committee acknowledges the work done by the committee of the *African American Heritage Hymnal* (GIA 2001) and its music editor, Rev. Nolan E. Williams, Jr. Theirs was the pioneering effort to represent African American musical performance practices on the printed page.

We also acknowledge J-Glenn Murray, SJ, author of the introductions to the rites and seasons; Jeffry Mickus, production coordinator, editor, engraver, and book layout; Philip Roberts, engraver and book layout; Joshua Evanovich, book layout; Clarence Reiels, proofreader; Rev. Ronald F. Krisman, text editor and indexer; Michael Boschert, permissions editor; and last but not least, Kelly Dobbs-Mickus for her counsel at virtually every step in this journey

Alec Harris
Publisher
Robert J. Batastini
Executive Editor and Project Director

Contents

Hymns and Songs

Indexes

Liturgy of the Hours

MORNING PRAISE

"From the rising of the sun till the going down of the same," the universal Church's way for how to pray is rooted in the traditions of our Jewish forbearers in the faith. African-American Catholics also pray this way. Anchored in this long-standing practice and no less rooted in our Black religious traditions, we come not to get, but to give God all the glory, praise, and honor. Whatever the day, whatever the trials and tribulations, whatever "dangers, toils, and snares"—"in the morning when we rise"— our way is to begin the day with prayer and praise. The sign of the cross, first traced on the Christian born again at baptism, is made again and again to start the new day and its powerful prayer. In songs and the psalms, in sacred scripture and intercessions, each one who prays and the community together find what it means to stand in the need of prayer at the dawning of a new day as a follower of Christ. The morning's prayer and praise gives the day its fresh meaning when, through the days and years, these prayers become our own—to God's greater glory.

Stand. All make the sign of the cross.

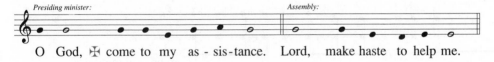

O God, ✠ come to my as-sis-tance. Lord, make haste to help me.

Glory to the Father, and to the Son, and to the Ho-ly Spir-it:

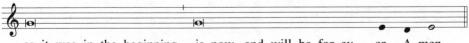

as it was in the beginning, is now, and will be for ev-er. A-men.

Added outside Lent:

Al - le - lu - ia.

Text: ICEL, © 1974

2 MORNING HYMN

This or another morning hymn, or one related to the season or feast, is sung.

1. Woke up this morn - in' with my mind,
2. No con-dem-na - tion with my mind, stayed on
3. Walk-in' and talk - in' with my mind,

mind, my mind was

Woke up this morn - in' with my mind,
Je - sus. No con-dem-na - tionwith my mind, stayed on
Walk-in' and talk - in' with my mind,

mind, my mind was

Woke up this morn - in' with my mind,
Je - sus. No con-dem-na - tion with my mind, stayed on
Walk-in' and talk - in' with my mind,

mind, my mind was

Je - sus. Hal - le - lu, hal - le - lu, hal - le - lu - jah.
*Praise the Lord, praise the Lord, praise the Lord.

*During Lent

Text: Congregational Praise Song
Tune: WITH MY MIND, 12 12 12 with hallelujahs; Congregational Praise Song, arr. by Evelyn Simpson-Curenton, b.1953, © 2000,
   GIA Publications, Inc.

PSALMODY

The singing of one or more psalms is central to morning prayer. Psalm 63, given on the next page, is one of the premier morning psalms. Psalm 51 (no. 30) is commonly substituted on Wednesday and Friday, as well as during Lent. Other appropriate psalms for morning are Psalms 8, 66, 95, 98 and 100.

PSALM 63

Sit

Refrain

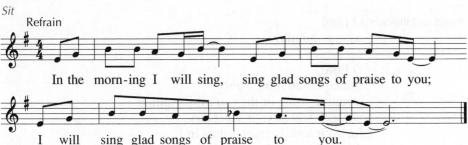

In the morn-ing I will sing, sing glad songs of praise to you;

I will sing glad songs of praise to you.

Text: *Praise God in Song*, © 1979, GIA Publications, Inc.
Music: Norah Duncan IV, © 2012, GIA Publications, Inc.

Verses

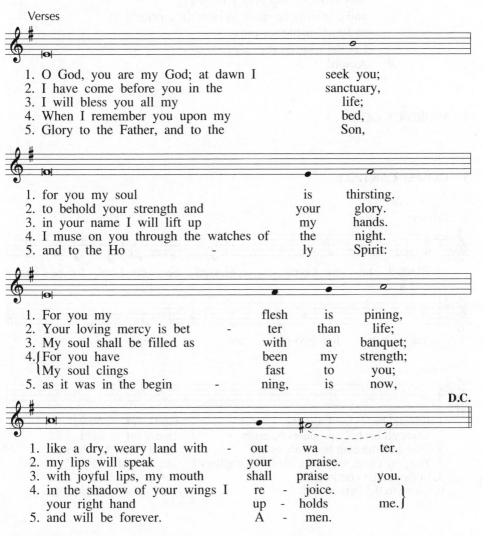

1. O God, you are my God; at dawn I   seek you;
2. I have come before you in the   sanctuary,
3. I will bless you all my   life;
4. When I remember you upon my   bed,
5. Glory to the Father, and to the   Son,

1. for you my soul   is   thirsting.
2. to behold your strength and   your   glory.
3. in your name I will lift up   my   hands.
4. I muse on you through the watches of   the   night.
5. and to the Ho   -   ly   Spirit:

1. For you my   flesh   is   pining,
2. Your loving mercy is bet   -   ter   than   life;
3. My soul shall be filled as   with   a   banquet;
4. { For you have   been   my   strength;
    { My soul clings   fast   to   you;
5. as it was in the begin   -   ning,   is   now,

D.C.

1. like a dry, weary land with   -   out   wa   -   ter.
2. my lips will speak   your   praise.
3. with joyful lips, my mouth   shall   praise   you.
4. in the shadow of your wings I   re   -   joice.
    your right hand   up   -   holds   me. }
5. and will be forever.   A   -   men.

Text: Psalm 63:2–9, *The Revised Grail Psalms*, © 2010, Conception Abbey and The Grail, admin. by GIA Publications, Inc.
Music: Michel Guimont, © 1994, 1998, GIA Publications, Inc.

PSALM PRAYER

Stand

Presiding Minister: O Lord,
what a morning!

O Lord,
source of unfailing light,
from the rising of the sun till its setting
we seek you in your sanctuary,
for your love is greater than life.
As we lift up holy hands in prayer,
hearts in songs of wonder, honor and praise,
may our worship give you glory,
and our lives be spent in humble service;
in Jesus' name we pray.
Let the Church say . . .

All: **Amen!**

4 WORD OF GOD

Sit

5 GOSPEL CANTICLE

Stand

Refrain

Blessed be the Lord, blessed be the Lord, for he has

come to his peo-ple and set them free.

Verses *All make the sign of the cross.*

1. Blessed be ✠ the Lord, the   God   of   Israel;
2. Through his holy prophets he prom - ised   of   old
3. This was the oath he swore to our   fa - ther Abraham:
4. You, my child, shall be called the prophet of   the   Most   High,
5. In the tender compassion   of   our   God
6. Glory to the Father, and   to   the   Son,

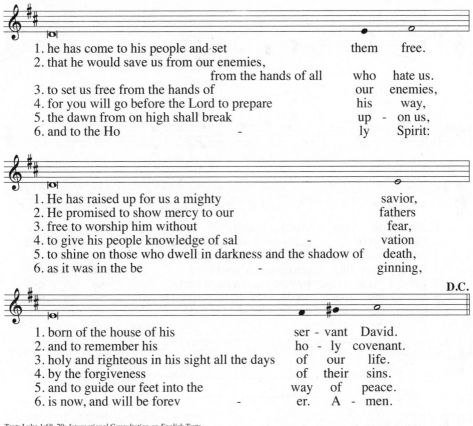

1. he has come to his people and set   them   free.
2. that he would save us from our enemies,
                   from the hands of all   who   hate us.
3. to set us free from the hands of   our   enemies,
4. for you will go before the Lord to prepare   his   way,
5. the dawn from on high shall break   up - on us,
6. and to the Ho   -   ly   Spirit:

1. He has raised up for us a mighty   savior,
2. He promised to show mercy to our   fathers
3. free to worship him without   fear,
4. to give his people knowledge of sal   -   vation
5. to shine on those who dwell in darkness and the shadow of   death,
6. as it was in the be   -   ginning,

D.C.

1. born of the house of his   ser - vant   David.
2. and to remember his   ho - ly   covenant.
3. holy and righteous in his sight all the days   of   our   life.
4. by the forgiveness   of   their   sins.
5. and to guide our feet into the   way   of   peace.
6. is now, and will be forev   -   er.   A - men.

Text: Luke 1:68–79; *International Consultation on English Texts*
Music: Refrain, Norah Duncan IV, © 2012, GIA Publications, Inc.; verses, Michel Guimont, © 1994, 1998, GIA Publications, Inc.

INTERCESSIONS   6

Moderately slow with rhythmic refrain

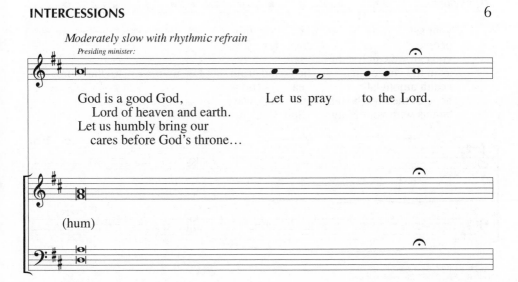

God is a good God,   Let us pray   to the Lord.
    Lord of heaven and earth.
Let us humbly bring our
    cares before God's throne...

(hum)

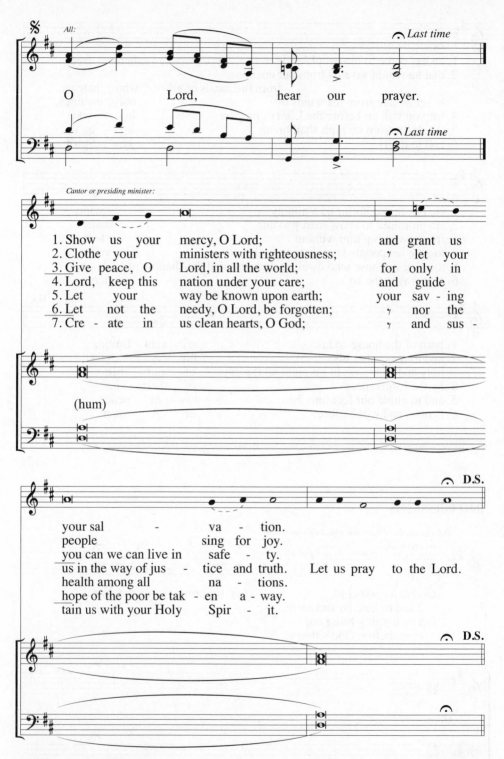

O Lord, hear our prayer.

Cantor or presiding minister:

1. Show us your mercy, O Lord; and grant us
2. Clothe your ministers with righteousness; let your
3. Give peace, O Lord, in all the world; for only in
4. Lord, keep this nation under your care; and guide
5. Let your way be known upon earth; your sav - ing
6. Let not the needy, O Lord, be forgotten; nor the
7. Cre - ate in us clean hearts, O God; and sus -

(hum)

your sal - va - tion.
people sing for joy.
you can we can live in safe - ty.
us in the way of jus - tice and truth. Let us pray to the Lord.
health among all na - tions.
hope of the poor be tak - en a - way.
tain us with your Holy Spir - it.

Text: *The Book of Common Prayer*
Music: Ray East, © 1987, GIA Publications, Inc.

THE LORD'S PRAYER

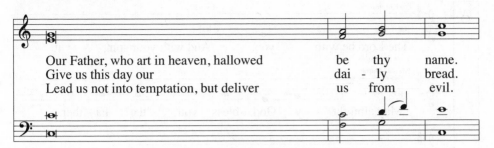

Our Father, who art in heaven, hallowed be thy name.
Give us this day our dai - ly bread.
Lead us not into temptation, but deliver us from evil.

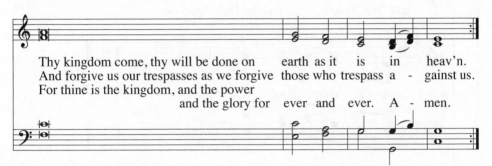

Thy kingdom come, thy will be done on earth as it is in heav'n.
And forgive us our trespasses as we forgive those who trespass a - gainst us.
For thine is the kingdom, and the power
    and the glory for ever and ever. A - men.

Music: C. E. Leslie; adapt. by Nolan Williams, Jr., b.1969, Evelyn Simpson-Curenton, b.1953, and Robert J. Fryson, © 2000, GIA Publications, Inc.

CONCLUDING PRAYER

Presiding Minister: God, you are a good God.
      You can do anything but fail.
      Yours is the morning.
      Yours is the evening too.
      Smile and shine on us at the dawning of this day.
      Hear our prayers, we humbly pray.
      Do what is to our benefit,
      the building up of your holy Church,
      the salvation of souls,
      and the glory of our Name.
      In Jesus' sweet name we pray.
      Let the Church say . . .
   All: **Amen!**

8 DISMISSAL

Text: ICEL, © 2010
Music: Amen, Michael Joncas, © 1979, GIA Publications, Inc.

9 *Dismissal, if the leader is not a priest or deacon:*

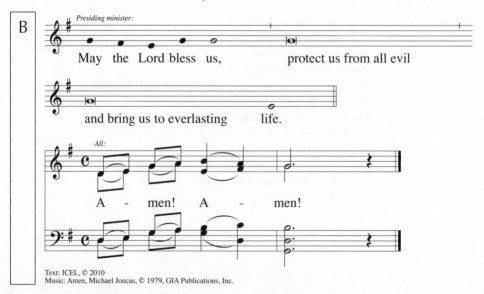

Text: ICEL, © 2010
Music: Amen, Michael Joncas, © 1979, GIA Publications, Inc.

All may conclude the celebration by exchanging a sign of peace.

EVENING PRAISE

Not unlike at morning, in the evening we gather again to give, not to get—to give God thanks for the day that is ending, at the setting of the sun. In the Church's earliest tradition, this began with the lighting of the lamps as darkness fell. In keeping with the early Church and the habit and custom of our ancestors who also stole away to hush harbors under the dark of night, we, too, gather to praise Christ who is "radiant Light. . . of God the Father's deathless face," the conqueror of slavery and oppression then and sin and death here and now.

The evening psalms and Mary's Song (the Magnificat) bring the day just past into focus for the Christian: "God has cast down the mighty from their thrones, and has lifted up the lowly"; "God has remembered the promise of mercy, the promise made to our ancestors." Prayers of intercession are almost always part of the universal Church's liturgy, but those which conclude evening prayer are especially important.

As day ends, we again and again in union with the whole Church throughout the earth lift up to God the cares and concerns, the moans and groans, faults and failures of all the world, remembering that someone somewhere sighs and cries: "somebody prayed for me, had me on their mind, took the time and prayed for me. I'm so glad they did." Such intercession is indeed the daily task and constant joy of all the baptized—to God's greater glory.

Stand. All make the sign of the cross.

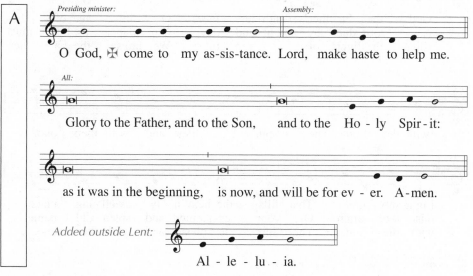

A

Presiding minister:

O God, ✠ come to my as-sis-tance.

Assembly:

Lord, make haste to help me.

All:

Glory to the Father, and to the Son, and to the Ho - ly Spir - it:

as it was in the beginning, is now, and will be for ev - er. A - men.

Added outside Lent:

Al - le - lu - ia.

Text: ICEL, © 1974

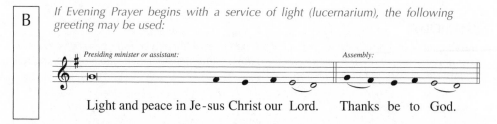

B

If Evening Prayer begins with a service of light (lucernarium), the following greeting may be used:

Presiding minister or assistant:

Light and peace in Je-sus Christ our Lord.

Assembly:

Thanks be to God.

11   EVENING HYMN

This or another evening hymn, or one related to the season or feast, is sung.

Descant:

3. Lord Je - sus Christ,   as   day - light   fades,   As

Melody:

1. O   ra - diant Light,   O Sun di - vine   Of
2. O   Son   of God,   the source of   life,   Praise
3. Lord Je - sus Christ,   as   day - light   fades,   As

shine   the   lights of   e - ven - tide,   We praise the   Fa - ther

God   the Fa - ther's death - less   face,   O   im - age of   the
is   your due   by   night and   day.   Our hap - py lips   must
shine   the lights of   e - ven - tide,   We praise   the Fa - ther

with the   Son,   The   Spir - it   blest, and   with them   one.

Light sub - lime   That fills   the heav'n - ly   dwell - ing   place.
raise the   strain   Of your   es - teemed and   splen - did   name.
with the   Son,   The Spir - it blest, and   with them   one.

Text: *Phos Hilaron*, Greek, c.200; tr. by William G. Storey, ©
Music: BOOTS, LM; Norah Duncan IV, © 2011, GIA Publications, Inc.

PSALMODY

The singing of one or more psalms is a central part of evening prayer. Psalm 141, given on the next page, is one of the premier evening psalms. Other appropriate psalms for evening are Psalms 19, 84, 91, 121, 130 and 145.

PSALM 141 / INCENSE PSALM

Sit

Refrain

My prayer shall rise like in - cense,

To verses | *Last time*

my hands like an eve - ning ob - la - tion.

Text: *Praise God in Song*, © 1979, GIA Publications, Inc., alt.
Music: Norah Duncan IV, © 1987, GIA Publications, Inc.

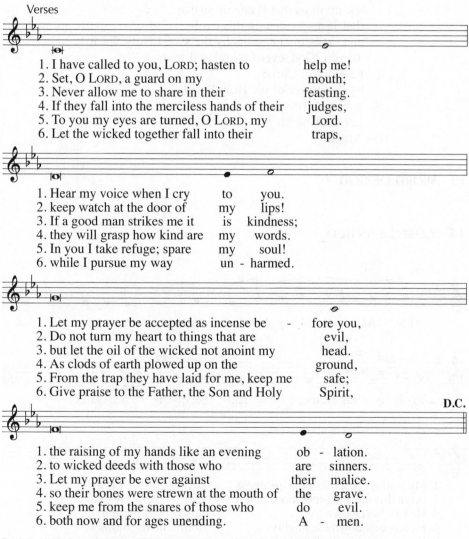

Verses

1. I have called to you, LORD; hasten to   help me!
2. Set, O LORD, a guard on my   mouth;
3. Never allow me to share in their   feasting.
4. If they fall into the merciless hands of their   judges,
5. To you my eyes are turned, O LORD, my   Lord.
6. Let the wicked together fall into their   traps,

1. Hear my voice when I cry   to   you.
2. keep watch at the door of   my   lips!
3. If a good man strikes me it   is   kindness;
4. they will grasp how kind are   my   words.
5. In you I take refuge; spare   my   soul!
6. while I pursue my way   un - harmed.

1. Let my prayer be accepted as incense be - fore you,
2. Do not turn my heart to things that are   evil,
3. but let the oil of the wicked not anoint my   head.
4. As clods of earth plowed up on the   ground,
5. From the trap they have laid for me, keep me   safe;
6. Give praise to the Father, the Son and Holy   Spirit,

D.C.

1. the raising of my hands like an evening   ob - lation.
2. to wicked deeds with those who   are   sinners.
3. Let my prayer be ever against   their   malice.
4. so their bones were strewn at the mouth of   the   grave.
5. keep me from the snares of those who   do   evil.
6. both now and for ages unending.   A - men.

Text: Psalm 141; *The Revised Grail Psalms*, © 2010, Conception Abbey and The Grail, admin. by GIA Publications, Inc., agent
Music: Michel Guimont, © 1994, 1998, GIA Publications, Inc.

PSALM PRAYER

Stand

Presiding Minister: Guardian of Israel, our shelter and shade,
you woke us this morning, clothed us,
and put us in our right minds.
And even more,
you have brought us thus far by faith
to this evening praise.

Now, O God,
may our prayers rise like incense before you,
and our own hands like an evening sacrifice.
Even now, O God,
stir up in us that flame of justice
that Jesus incited on this earth,
and rages in our hearts by the sweet Holy Spirit.
To you, God, ever faithful and true,
be glory in Christ
by the power of the Holy Spirit,
now and forever.
Let the Church say . . .

All: **Amen!**

13 WORD OF GOD

Sit

14 GOSPEL CANTICLE

Stand

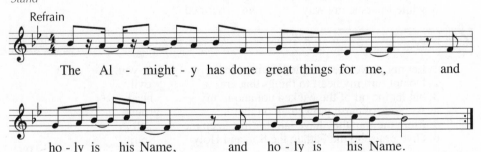

Refrain

The Al - might - y has done great things for me, and ho - ly is his Name, and ho - ly is his Name.

Verses *All make the sign of the cross.*

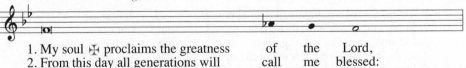

1. My soul ✠ proclaims the greatness of the Lord,
2. From this day all generations will call me blessed:
3. He has mercy on those who fear him
4. He has cast down the mighty from their thrones,
5. He has come to the help of his ser - vant Israel
6. Glory to the Father, and to the Son,

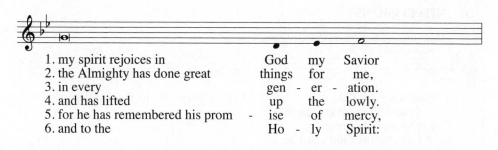

1. my spirit rejoices in   God   my   Savior
2. the Almighty has done great   things   for   me,
3. in every   gen - er - ation.
4. and has lifted   up   the   lowly.
5. for he has remembered his prom - ise   of   mercy,
6. and to the   Ho - ly   Spirit:

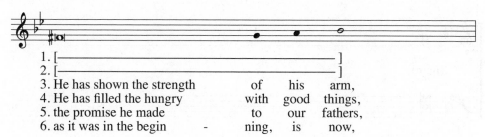

1. [——————————————————]
2. [——————————————————]
3. He has shown the strength   of   his   arm,
4. He has filled the hungry   with   good   things,
5. the promise he made   to   our   fathers,
6. as it was in the begin - ning,   is   now,

D.C.

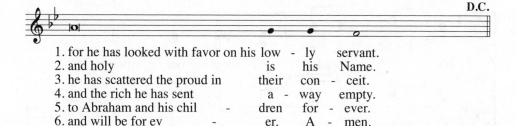

1. for he has looked with favor on his low - ly   servant.
2. and holy   is   his   Name.
3. he has scattered the proud in   their   con - ceit.
4. and the rich he has sent   a - way   empty.
5. to Abraham and his chil - dren   for - ever.
6. and will be for ev - er.   A - men.

Text: Luke 1:46–55; *International Consultation on English Texts*
Music: Norah Duncan IV, © 2012, GIA Publications, Inc.

15 INTERCESSIONS

Moderately slow with rhythmic refrain

Presiding minister:

God is a good God,
Lord of heaven and earth.
Let us humbly bring our
cares before God's throne…

Let us pray to the Lord.

(hum)

All:

O Lord, hear our prayer. *Last time*

(hum) *Last time*

Cantor or presiding minister:

1. Save your people, Lord, and bless your inheritance; govern and up-
2. Give peace to your Church and to the whole world; make us your
3. Grant us for-giveness of our sins and offenses; have mer-cy
4. Strengthen our com-munion with all your saints; bind us to-
5. Heal the sick and comfort the lonely; re-lieve the
6. Re-mem-ber all who have died in your mercy; wel-come
7. In you, Lord, is our hope; and we

(hum)

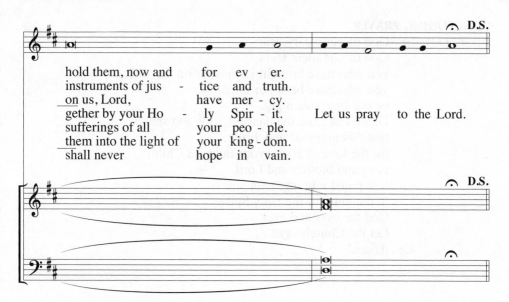

hold them, now and for ev - er.
instruments of jus - tice and truth.
on us, Lord, have mer - cy.
gether by your Ho - ly Spir - it. Let us pray to the Lord.
sufferings of all your peo - ple.
them into the light of your king - dom.
shall never hope in vain.

Text: Adapted from *The Book of Common Prayer*
Music: Ray East, © 1987, GIA Publications, Inc.

THE LORD'S PRAYER   16

Our Father, who art in heaven, hallowed be thy name.
Give us this day our dai - ly bread.
Lead us not into temptation, but deliver us from evil.

Thy kingdom come, thy will be done on earth as it is in heav'n.
And forgive us our trespasses as we forgive those who trespass a - gainst us.
For thine is the kingdom, and the power
and the glory for ever and ever. A - men.

Music: C. E. Leslie; adapt. by Nolan Williams, Jr., b.1969, Evelyn Simpson-Curenton, b.1953, and Robert J. Fryson, © 2000, GIA Publications, Inc.

CONCLUDING PRAYER

Presiding Minister: God of our weary years,
God of our silent tears,
you who have brought us thus far on the way;
you who have been our might:
be our light this night.
Defend us from the dangers, toils and snares
that this nightfall may bring;
for the love of Jesus, your Beloved Child,
our good brother and Lord,
living and reigning with you
in the unity of the Holy Spirit,
God for ever and ever.
Let the Church say . . .

All: **Amen!**

17   DISMISSAL

Text: ICEL, © 2010
Music: Amen, Michael Joncas, © 1979, GIA Publications, Inc.

Dismissal, if the leader is not a priest or deacon:

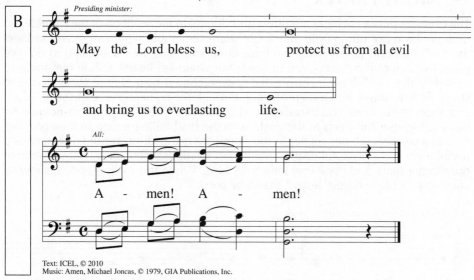

Text: ICEL, © 2010
Music: Amen, Michael Joncas, © 1979, GIA Publications, Inc.

All may conclude the celebration by exchanging a sign of peace.

19 NIGHT PRAYER

The Church's prayers at night are direct and simple. In the tradition of the Church and in the folkways of our people, Black Christians remember with sorrow and sadness the day's hurt and harm—what we have done and what we have failed to do. We place this before the mercy-seat, bringing our wounded hearts, telling our anguish, confident that earth has no sorrow that heaven cannot heal. Before surrendering to sleep, there is prayer for God's protection through the night and an expression of acceptance: "Now, Lord, you may dismiss your servant." The night prayer concludes by binding together the sleep of this night with the final falling asleep in the Lord, our rock in a weary land, our shelter in the storm: "May the all-powerful Lord grant us a restful night and a peaceful death." Night's last words are often a gentle invocation of our Mother Mary and her sweet little baby boy, "When this exile is ended, show us your womb's blessed fruit, Jesus." May it be so!

Stand. All make the sign of the cross.

Presiding minister: O God, ✠ come to my as-sis-tance. *Assembly:* Lord, make haste to help me.

All: Glory to the Father, and to the Son, and to the Ho-ly Spir-it:

as it was in the beginning, is now, and will be for ev - er. A-men.

Added outside Lent:

Al - le - lu - ia.

Text: ICEL, © 1974

A brief examination of conscience may be made. At its conclusion, the following may be said:

> Optional
>
> **I confess to almighty God**
> **and to you, my brothers and sisters,**
> **that I have greatly sinned,**
> **in my thoughts and in my words,**
> **in what I have done and in what I have failed to do,**
> *All strike their breast as they say:*
> **through my fault, through my fault,**
> **through my most grievous fault;**
> **therefore I ask blessed Mary ever-Virgin,**
> **all the Angels and Saints,**
> **and you, my brothers and sisters,**
> **to pray for me to the Lord our God.**

HYMN

This or another evening hymn, or one related to the season or feast, is sung.

1. A - bide with me; fast falls the e - ven - tide;
2. Swift to its close ebbs out life's lit - tle day;
3. I need thy pres - ence ev - 'ry pass - ing hour;
4. I fear no foe, with thee at hand to bless;
5. Hold thou thy cross be - fore my clos - ing eyes;

The dark - ness deep - ens; Lord, with me a - bide
Earth's joys grow dim; its glo - ries pass a - way;
What but thy grace can foil the tempt - er's pow'r?
Ills have no weight, and tears no bit - ter - ness.
Shine through the gloom and point me to the skies;

When oth - er help - ers fail and com - forts flee,
Change and de - cay in all a - round I see;
Who, like thy - self, my guide and stay can be?
Where is death's sting? Where, grave, your vic - to - ry?
Heav'n's morn - ing breaks, and earth's vain shad - ows flee;

Help of the help - less, O a - bide with me.
O thou who chang - est not, a - bide with me.
Through cloud and sun - shine, Lord, a - bide with me.
I tri - umph still, if thou a - bide with me.
In life, in death, O Lord, a - bide with me.

Text: Henry F. Lyte, 1793–1847
Tune: EVENTIDE, 10 10 10 10; William H. Monk, 1823–1889; arr. by Evelyn Simpson-Curenton, b.1953, © 2000, GIA Publications, Inc.

PSALMODY

The proper psalms for night prayer are: Sunday, Psalm 91 (no. 35); Monday, Psalm 86 (no. 33); Tuesday, Psalm 143 (no. 42); Wednesday, Psalms 31 and 130 (nos. 29 and 40); Thursday, Psalm 16 (no. 27); Friday, Psalm 88 (no. 34); Saturday, Psalms 4 and 134 (nos. 25 and 41).

Sit

21 WORD OF GOD

22 RESPONSORY

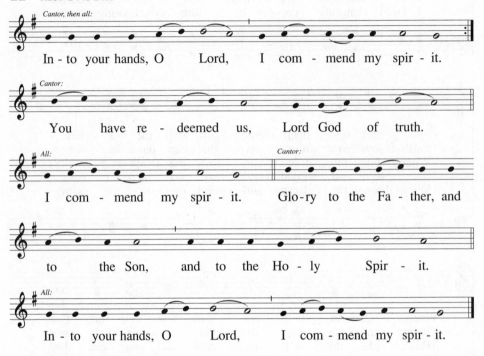

Cantor, then all:
In-to your hands, O Lord, I com-mend my spir-it.

Cantor:
You have re-deemed us, Lord God of truth.

All:
I com-mend my spir-it.

Cantor:
Glo-ry to the Fa-ther, and to the Son, and to the Ho-ly Spir-it.

All:
In-to your hands, O Lord, I com-mend my spir-it.

Text: *Liturgy of the Hours,* © 1974, ICEL
Music: Sarum tone, adapt. by Richard Proulx, © 1986, GIA Publications, Inc.

23 GOSPEL CANTICLE

Stand

Antiphon

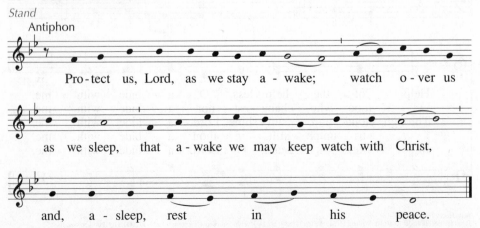

Pro-tect us, Lord, as we stay a-wake; watch o-ver us as we sleep, that a-wake we may keep watch with Christ, and, a-sleep, rest in his peace.

Verse 1 *All make the sign of the cross.*

1. Lord, ✠ now you let your ser - vant go in peace:

D.C.

your word has been ful - filled.

Verse 2

2. My own eyes have seen the sal - va - tion

D.C.

which you have prepared in the sight of ev - 'ry peo - ple.

Verse 3

3. A light to re - veal you to the na - tions

D.C.

and the glory of your peo - ple Is - ra - el.

Verse 4

4. Glory to the Fa - ther, and to the Son, and to the

Ho - ly Spir - it: as it was in the be - gin - ning,

D.C.

is now, and will be for ev - er. A - men.

Text: Antiphon from *Liturgy of the Hours*, © 1974, ICEL; verses, Luke 2:29–32; *International Consultation on English Texts*
Music: Sarum tone, adapt. by Richard Proulx, © 1986, GIA Publications, Inc.

CONCLUDING PRAYER
All respond: **Amen.**

24 CONCLUSION

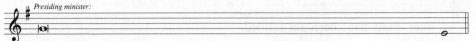

Presiding minister:

May the all-powerful Lord grant us a restful night and a peaceful death.

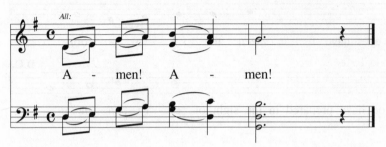

All:

A - men! A - men!

Text: ICEL, © 1974
Music: Amen, Michael Joncas, © 1979, GIA Publications, Inc.

A Marian antiphon, such as "Salve Regína / Hail, Queen of Heaven," no. 723, may follow.

Psalm 4: Have Mercy, Lord   25

Refrain

Have mer - cy, Lord. Have mer - cy, Lord.

Have mer - cy, Lord, and hear my prayer.

Text: *Liturgy of the Hours,* © 1974, ICEL
Music: Norah Duncan IV, © 2012, GIA Publications, Inc.

Verses

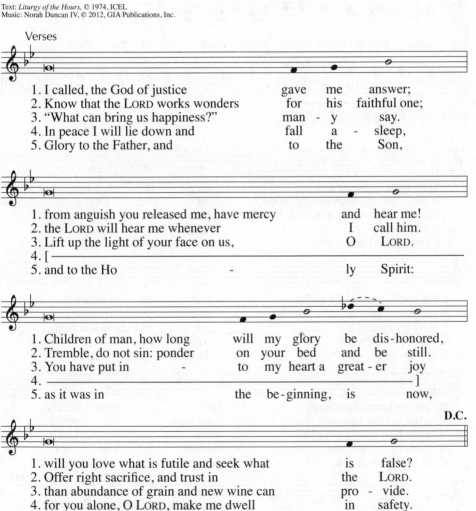

1. I called, the God of justice gave me answer;
2. Know that the LORD works wonders for his faithful one;
3. "What can bring us happiness?" man - y say.
4. In peace I will lie down and fall a - sleep,
5. Glory to the Father, and to the Son,

1. from anguish you released me, have mercy and hear me!
2. the LORD will hear me whenever I call him.
3. Lift up the light of your face on us, O LORD.
4. [—————————————————————————————
5. and to the Ho - ly Spirit:

1. Children of man, how long will my glory be dis-honored,
2. Tremble, do not sin: ponder on your bed and be still.
3. You have put in - to my heart a great - er joy
4. —————————————————————————————]
5. as it was in the be-ginning, is now,

D.C.

1. will you love what is futile and seek what is false?
2. Offer right sacrifice, and trust in the LORD.
3. than abundance of grain and new wine can pro - vide.
4. for you alone, O LORD, make me dwell in safety.
5. and will be for ever. A - men.

Text: Psalm 4; *The Revised Grail Psalms,* © 2010, Conception Abbey and The Grail, admin. by GIA Publications, Inc.
Music: Rawn Harbor, © 1985, Rawn Harbor

26 Psalm 8: O Lord, Our God

Refrain

O Lord, our God, how won-der-ful your name, how won-der-ful your name in all the earth!

Text: *Lectionary for Mass,* © 1969, 1981, 1997, ICEL
Music: Nicholas Palmer, © 2012, GIA Publications, Inc.

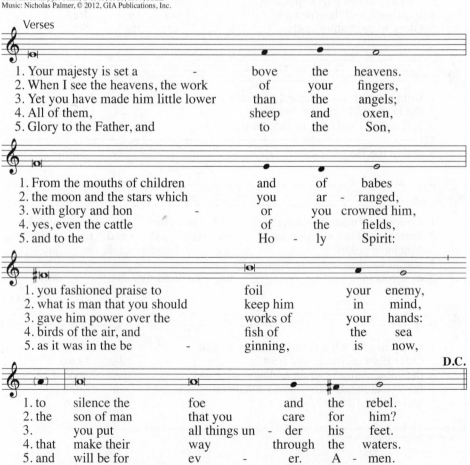

Verses

1. Your majesty is set a - bove the heavens.
2. When I see the heavens, the work of your fingers,
3. Yet you have made him little lower than the angels;
4. All of them, sheep and oxen,
5. Glory to the Father, and to the Son,

1. From the mouths of children and of babes
2. the moon and the stars which you ar - ranged,
3. with glory and hon - or you crowned him,
4. yes, even the cattle of the fields,
5. and to the Ho - ly Spirit:

1. you fashioned praise to foil your enemy,
2. what is man that you should keep him in mind,
3. gave him power over the works of your hands:
4. birds of the air, and fish of the sea
5. as it was in the be - ginning, is now,

D.C.

1. to silence the foe and the rebel.
2. the son of man that you care for him?
3. you put all things un - der his feet.
4. that make their way through the waters.
5. and will be for ev - er. A - men.

Text: Psalm 8; *The Revised Grail Psalms,* © 2010, Conception Abbey and The Grail, admin. by GIA Publications, Inc., agent
Music: Michel Guimont, © 1994, 1998, GIA Publications, Inc.

Psalm 16: In You, My God   27

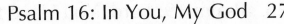

Refrain

In you, my God, my bod-y will rest, my bod-y will rest in hope.

Text: *Liturgy of the Hours*, © 1974, ICEL
Music: Norah Duncan IV, © 2012, GIA Publications, Inc.

Verses

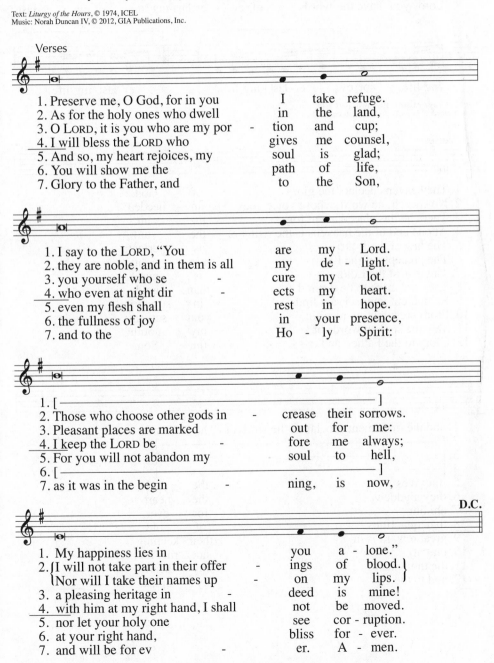

1. Preserve me, O God, for in you   I   take   refuge.
2. As for the holy ones who dwell   in   the   land,
3. O LORD, it is you who are my por - tion   and   cup;
4. I will bless the LORD who   gives   me   counsel,
5. And so, my heart rejoices, my   soul   is   glad;
6. You will show me the   path   of   life,
7. Glory to the Father, and   to   the   Son,

1. I say to the LORD, "You   are   my   Lord.
2. they are noble, and in them is all   my   de - light.
3. you yourself who se - cure   my   lot.
4. who even at night dir - ects   my   heart.
5. even my flesh shall   rest   in   hope.
6. the fullness of joy   in   your   presence,
7. and to the   Ho - ly   Spirit:

1. [——————————————————]
2. Those who choose other gods in - crease   their   sorrows.
3. Pleasant places are marked   out   for   me:
4. I keep the LORD be - fore   me   always;
5. For you will not abandon my   soul   to   hell,
6. [——————————————————]
7. as it was in the begin - ning,   is   now,

D.C.

1. My happiness lies in   you   a - lone."
2. {I will not take part in their offer - ings   of   blood.}
   {Nor will I take their names up - on   my   lips.}
3. a pleasing heritage in - deed   is   mine!
4. with him at my right hand, I shall   not   be   moved.
5. nor let your holy one   see   cor - ruption.
6. at your right hand,   bliss   for - ever.
7. and will be for ev - er.   A - men.

Text: Psalm 16: *The Revised Grail Psalms*, © 2010, Conception Abbey and The Grail, admin. by GIA Publications, Inc., agent
Music: Stanbrook Abbey, © 1984, The Benedictine Sisters of Stanbrook Abbey

28 Psalm 19: Lord, You Have the Words

Lord, you have the words of ev - er-last-ing life, of ev - er-last-ing life, of ev - er-last-ing life. er-last-ing life.

Text: *Lectionary for Mass*, © 1969, 1981, 1997, ICEL
Music: Kenneth W. Louis, © 2012, GIA Publications, Inc.

Verses

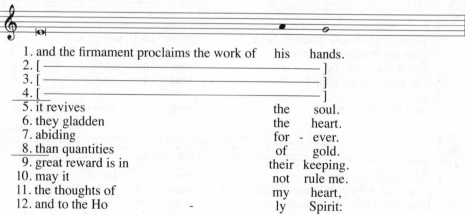

1. The heavens declare the glory of God,
2. No speech, no word, whose voice goes un - heeded;
3. There he has placed a tent for the sun;
4. At one end of the heavens is the rising of the sun;
5. The law of the LORD is perfect;
6. The precepts of the LORD are right;
7. The fear of the LORD is pure,
8. They are more to be desired than gold,
9. So in them your servant finds in - struction;
10. From presumption restrain your servant;
11. May the spoken words of my mouth,
12. Glory to the Father, and to the Son,

1. and the firmament proclaims the work of his hands.
2. [————————————————]
3. [————————————————]
4. [————————————————]
5. it revives the soul.
6. they gladden the heart.
7. abiding for - ever.
8. than quantities of gold.
9. great reward is in their keeping.
10. may it not rule me.
11. the thoughts of my heart,
12. and to the Ho - ly Spirit: